Illustrated Stories *from the* Bible

Volume 2

AUTHORS
George and Marilyn Durrant
Former Professor of Ancient Scriptures

Educational Doctorate

ARTIST AND ART DIRECTOR
Vernon Murdock
Artist Illustrator

Bachelor of Fine Arts
Graduate Work, University of Madrid,
*   Spain*

CORRELATORS AND DIRECTORS
Steven R. Shallenberger, *President*
Community Press, Wisdom House, Eagle
*   Marketing Corporation*

Bachelor of Science; Accounting, Business.
SCMP, Graduate School of Business, Harvard
*   University.*

Paul R. Cheesman
Director of Scripture in Religious Study Center
Chaplain, U.S. Navy

Doctor of Religious Education

Lael J. Woodbury
Chairman, National Committee on Royalties,
*   American Theatre Association*

Doctorate of Theater, University of Illinois

ADVISORS
Dale T. Tingey
Director American Indian Services and
*   Research Center*

Doctor of Philosophy, Guidance and
*   Counseling; Washington State University*

Reverend Raymond E. Ansel
Ordained Minister

Southwestern Assemblies of God College, Texas
*   Berean Bible School, Missouri*

Millie Foster Cheesman
Writer, Poetess

M.J. Bardon
Missionary-Pastor, Grace Baptist Church

Th. M. Clarksville School of Theology
*   Clarksville, Tennessee*

Reverend William R. Schroeder
United Church of Christ

United Theological Seminary of the Twin Cities
*   New Brighton, Minnesota*

THIRD EDITION VOLUME 2, MAY 1982

Lithographed in U.S.A.
by
COMMUNITY PRESS, INC.
P.O. Box 1229
Antioch, California 94509

A Member of
The American Bookseller's Association
New York, New York

Now these are the commandments, the statutes, and the judgments, which the Lord your God commanded to teach you, that ye might do them in the land whither ye go to possess it:

That thou mightest fear the Lord thy God, to keep all his statutes and his commandments, which I command thee, thou, and thy son, and thy son's son, all the days of thy life; and that thy days may be prolonged.

Hear therefore, O Israel, and observe to do it; that it may be well with thee, and that ye may increase mightily, as the Lord God of thy fathers hath promised thee, in the land that floweth with milk and honey.

Deuteronomy 6:1-3

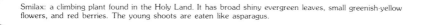

Smilax: a climbing plant found in the Holy Land. It has broad shiny evergreen leaves, small greenish-yellow flowers, and red berries. The young shoots are eaten like asparagus.

Dedicated to boys and girls throughout the world and to all who love the Bible.

A nondenominational work.

CONTENTS

Our story so far . . .

In Volume One we read of the creation of the earth and the beautiful Garden of Eden. We learned how Adam and Eve were sent from there to another place where they had to work hard for their food. We read how some of their children obeyed them, and the sad things that happened to those who did not listen to their parents.

The story of Noah and the great ark was next, which was followed by the building of the great tower of Babel.

Then we began reading about the prophet Abraham and how God taught and helped this wonderful man. We learned of Abraham's travels to find the Promised Land, about a man named Lot and his selfishness, and also about Lot's wife turning to salt. Remember the story of Abraham's son Isaac, who was to be sacrificed but was saved when the Lord learned that Abraham was willing to sacrifice his only beloved son for the Lord?

We also read how Isaac received a wife through an answer to his servant's prayer. Then followed the story of the twins (named Esau and Jacob) born to Isaac and Rebekah, and how Isaac gave Jacob the family leadership (birthright) belonging to Esau. The next story was of Jacob, who worked for many years to earn Rachel as his wife.

Now we will continue into Volume Two and see what happens when Jacob and his brother Esau meet once again.

GOD BLESSES TWO BROTHERS
Genesis Chapters 32, 33

Jacob remembered the night in the mountains many years before, when God had promised him that someday he would be given the land where he had lived with his father, Isaac. He was still homesick and wanted to return home, but there was one big reason why he couldn't. That reason was Esau—the brother who had planned to kill Jacob because he felt his younger brother should not have been given the birthright to lead the family.

Finally, after twenty years in Haran, Jacob decided he would go home, having faith that God would protect him. All people should be as Jacob and know that even though the future is unknown, they need not fear. As long as they are trying to do the right thing, God will protect them.

Jacob and his large family (including all twelve sons) departed from Haran, just as grandfather Abraham had done many years before, and headed toward the Promised Land. They were going home.

As the travelers came closer to the mountains and valleys of Jacob's boyhood, Jacob probably wondered, "What will Esau do? Will he try to kill me?" Still he journeyed on, praying with each mile that all would be well.

Finally those of Jacob's men who had been sent out in front as scouts saw Esau with 400 of his men. Jacob was "greatly afraid and distressed." Four hundred was a large number of men, so he divided his people into two groups. If Esau attacked one group, perhaps at least the other group could escape.

Again Jacob prayed for wisdom to know what to do. He also asked God to bless Esau that he would not want to destroy Jacob and his people.

Jacob decided to send a great gift of over 500 of his finest goats and cattle to his brother. He told his men to go ahead of the caravan and give these to Esau.

That night was one of worry and fear. Tomorrow would be the day when either Jacob and his entire family would be destroyed or everything would turn out right. Jacob went to a place where he could be alone and began to pray. He asked God to forgive him of all he had ever done wrong. He prayed to God just as he would have spoken to his earthly father, and he begged and pleaded for God to be with him.

Suddenly someone grabbed him. He had never felt anyone as strong and he tried to free himself. There was a mighty struggle as on and on the two wrestled! Jacob's thigh was thrown out of joint, which caused great pain, but the battle went on.

By daybreak Jacob realized that the man with whom he was struggling was not just a man but a heavenly person. Jacob, not wishing to let the person go, held on tightly. The person said, "Let me go, for the day breaketh." Jacob answered, "I will not let thee go, except thou bless me."

The heavenly messenger then asked Jacob his name. After Jacob had replied, he heard these words. "Thy name shall be called no more Jacob, but Israel." The name Israel means "Prince of God."

Jacob asked this heavenly person his name but the man did not reply. Jacob later said, ". . . I have seen God face to face. . . ."

It was morning now, and Jacob was no longer afraid. Then Esau appeared at a distance, approaching closer and closer. Jacob ran forward, then stopped and bowed himself before his brother seven times. "And Esau ran to meet him, and embraced him . . . and kissed him: and they wept."

The past was over. The two brothers were friends once again. God had caused the hearts of each to change and life was good again for both of them. Hate will make anyone miserable, but love and forgiveness always restore happiness.

THINK ABOUT IT

1. What is the biggest problem you have ever had that caused you to be afraid of what might happen?
2. Did you pray and ask Heavenly Father to help you so that things would go well? What finally happened?
3. Why do you feel that Esau forgave Jacob?
4. What did Esau gain by forgiving instead of fighting?

ALL SEEMS LOST
Genesis Chapter 37

Everyone likes to have beautiful clothes. Jacob, now called Israel, probably wanted all his children to dress well. He had a beautiful coat made for his favorite son. This son's name was Joseph.

The reason Jacob loved Joseph so much was that he was Rachel's son. He had worked many years for Rachel, and although he had other older sons, they were Leah's or one of the handmaids' children rather than Rachel's. At last a son had been born of Rachel and had been named Joseph.

The ten older sons didn't really like the ways Jacob showed favor to Joseph; so *of course* they didn't like it when their father gave Joseph the coat of many colors.

Joseph was an honest young man who always told the truth, even if it got others and sometimes himself in trouble. Once when he saw his brothers doing things they shouldn't have been doing, he went home and told his father. This caused the ten older brothers to hate him more. Only his younger brother, Benjamin, liked him.

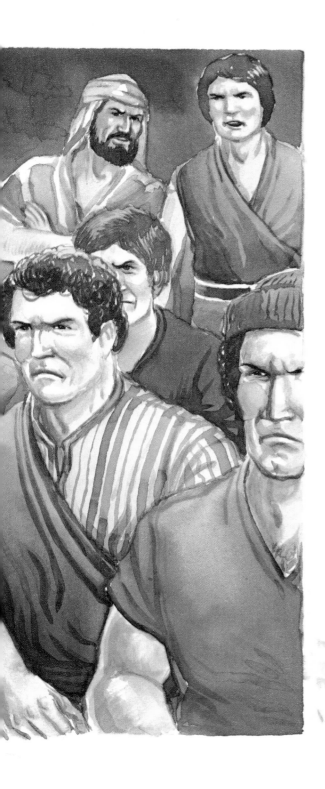

Often Joseph dreamed. In one of his dreams he saw that he and his eleven brothers each had a sheaf of grain. He saw the sheaves of his eleven brothers bowed down to his sheaf, and when he told his brothers about it, they were upset and said, "Shalt thou indeed reign over us?" This dream, and many other such dreams, caused his brothers to hate him.

Joseph's honesty, his brothers' hatred toward him, and Jacob's (Israel's) love for him all brought about the following incredible episode.

One day the ten brothers were many miles from home tending the family's flocks of animals. Jacob (Israel) was wondering how things were going, so he sent Joseph to find them.

When the brothers saw Joseph coming, hatred and anger rose up in their hearts. As Joseph approached, he smiled and shouted to his brothers, thinking they would be glad to see him. He soon found they were not pleased at all that he had come.

Suddenly shock and fear found their way into Joseph's heart. His brothers grabbed him and, while shouting angry words, carried him along. He fought, but it was no use; there were too many of them. Soon they approached a deep hole in the ground and he felt himself thrown down into it. His body fell hard against the bottom of the pit. He could hear his brothers talking above, saying, "That's the last we will ever see of him." Joseph was helpless and realized his brothers planned to let him die there.

But God knew what was happening and wouldn't let his great servant die. The brothers decided to get Joseph out of the pit and sell him as a slave to a passing caravan of Ishmaelites on its way to Egypt. They probably felt that, cruel as this was, it was better for him than dying in the pit.

Joseph was glad to be pulled from the dark hole but was again very sad as he saw his brothers receive money from these strangers. He then realized his fate was to be sold as a slave.

As he was bound and led away, he may have shouted, "Don't let them take me. What will father do?" But now, because of the distance, his brothers could hear his voice no longer. Soon the desert caravan was gone from sight—and Joseph with it.

The brothers stood and talked. A few of them may have felt a little remorse. It's hard to do evil deeds without feeling sorry afterwards. What would they tell their heartbroken father?

A lamb was killed and its blood was smeared on Joseph's coat. The ten brothers then told their father a lie: "Animals ate your son for here is his coat. You can see his blood." Thus the wicked brothers sinned again by lying, adding that sin to the one committed by selling Joseph as a slave. Joseph's father was heartbroken; his beloved son Joseph was dead!

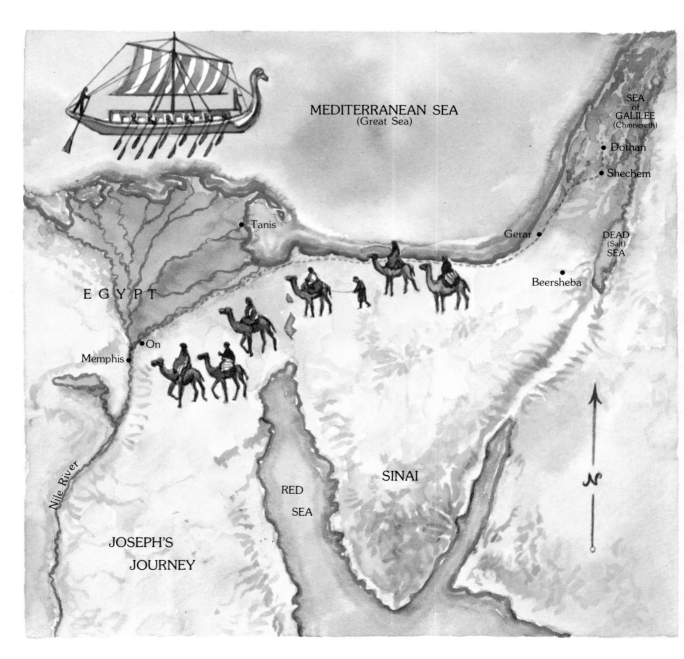

MEDITERRANEAN SEA
(Great Sea)

SEA of GALILEE
(Chinnereth)

• Dothan

• Shechem

• Tanis

Gerar •

DEAD
(Salt)
SEA

• Beersheba

E G Y P T

•On

Memphis •

SINAI

RED
SEA

Nile River

N

JOSEPH'S

JOURNEY

FROM THE BOTTOM
TO THE TOP
Genesis Chapters 39-41

Poor Joseph! His father couldn't help him, his brothers wouldn't help him, and he couldn't do much to help himself. Who could help this lonely young man in the mysterious land of the pyramids? The men of the caravan arrived in Egypt and, wanting to get rid of Joseph, took him to the slave market to sell him. Joseph closed his eyes as he listened to the auctioneer call out his name. He silently called out, "Please, dear God, help me." And God did help him.

"He's yours!" the auctioneer shouted. Potiphar, the captain of the king's guard, smiled as he told Joseph to follow him. For the next few months Jacob's favorite son did exactly what his new master told him to do. He did it so well that Potiphar soon made Joseph chief over all the other slaves working in his house.

Joseph was still homesick, but because God was with him he was beginning to feel happy in Egypt. He liked the work he was doing and he liked Potiphar. Then Satan tryed to destroy Joseph. Potiphar's wife thought Joseph was handsome and wanted him to be her secret boyfriend. Joseph was shocked and told her that he would not. In her anger she decided to get Joseph into trouble by telling her husband that Joseph was trying to be her lover.

Potiphar believed his lying wife and had Joseph thrown into prison. At this point Satan probably thought he had once again destroyed one of God's servants. However Satan did not realize that Joseph was a very determined, faithful, hardworking young man who believed in God so much that he knew God would help him, even in a dark prison.

In time Joseph, because he was such a pleasant, hard worker, was put in charge of all the other prisoners. They all liked him because he was friendly and good to them. Two of his cell mates in the prison had once been the baker and the butler to Pharaoh (king of Egypt).

One night the butler dreamed that he again prepared wine for Pharaoh. On that same night the baker dreamed that he once again baked bread for Pharaoh, but birds came and ate it. Feeling Joseph was so wise, they told him about their dreams and asked him what they meant. God was with Joseph as Joseph told the butler, "You will soon be free and go back to work for Pharaoh." The news for the baker was not so pleasant. Joseph told this poor man that in three days he would be killed.

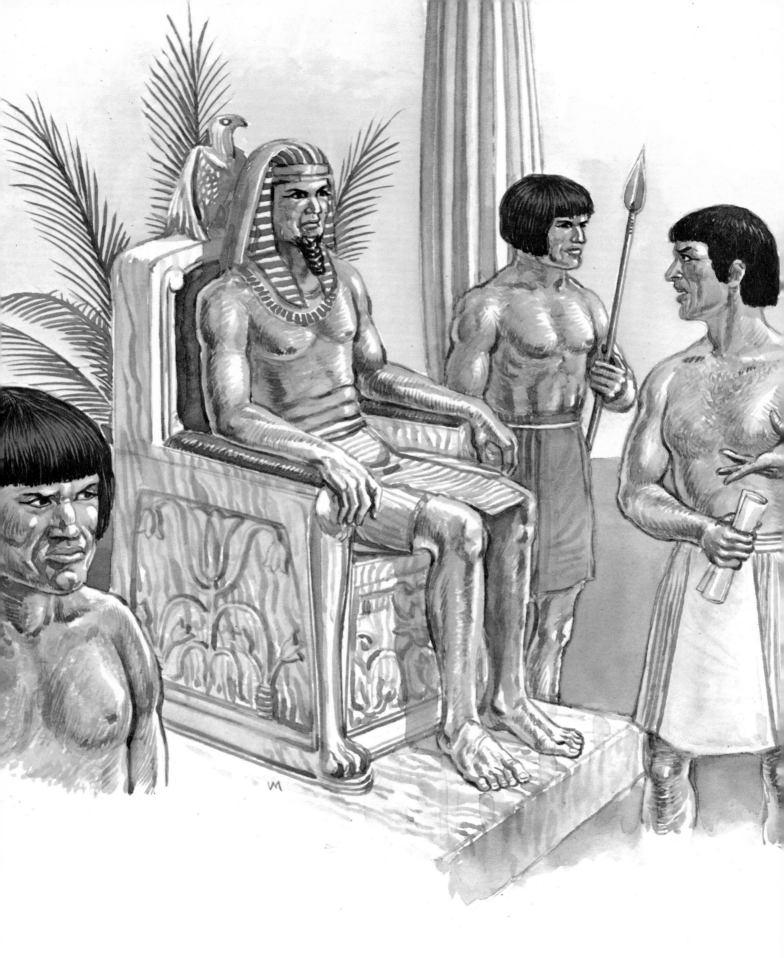

Joseph was indeed a prophet. In three days the baker was killed and the butler went back to work for Pharaoh. Joseph had asked the butler beforehand, "When you get back to the palace be sure and tell Pharaoh about me." This the butler forgot to do until one day Pharaoh had a very strange dream. He told his servants about his dream and asked them, "What does it mean?" Everyone said they didn't know until finally the butler remembered Joseph.

When Joseph learned that Pharaoh wanted to see him, ". . . he shaved *himself,* and changed his raiment [clothes]. . . ."

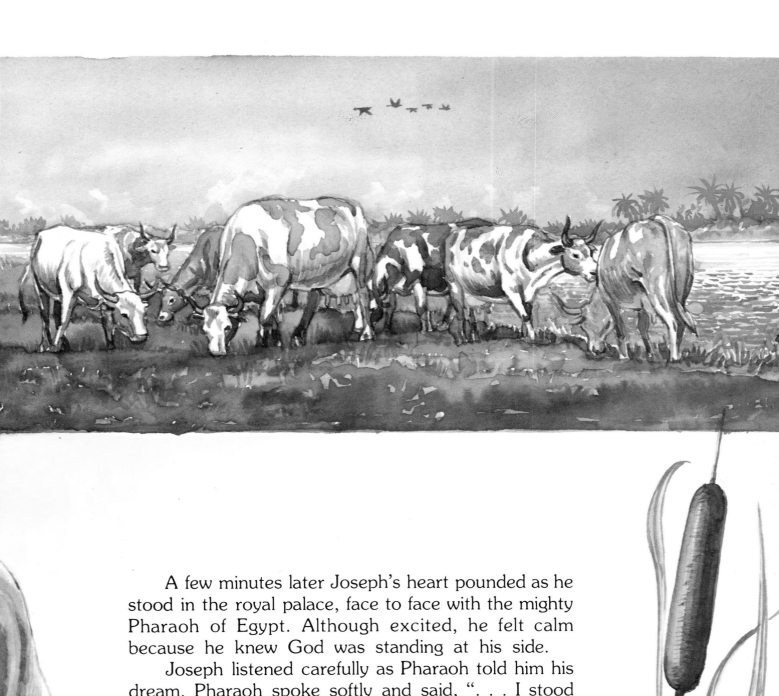

A few minutes later Joseph's heart pounded as he stood in the royal palace, face to face with the mighty Pharaoh of Egypt. Although excited, he felt calm because he knew God was standing at his side.

Joseph listened carefully as Pharaoh told him his dream. Pharaoh spoke softly and said, ". . . I stood upon the bank of the river: And, behold, there came up out of the river seven kine [cows], fatfleshed. . . ."

43

44

Pharaoh continued that seven thin kine (cows) also came out of the river and ate the fat ones. Later in his dream he mentioned he saw seven fat ears of corn eaten by seven thin ears of corn. With such a strange dream, it was no wonder no one had been able to tell him what it meant.

But God knew what it meant, and when God wanted his people to know something he told a prophet. Joseph, being a prophet, was inspired by God to say: "Behold, there come seven years of great plenty . . . [and] after them seven years of famine . . . "

Joseph further explained to Pharaoh, "You should store food for the next seven good years, because after that there will be a time when the wind will blow and it will not rain, and there will be no food grown.

Joseph also told Pharaoh, "You should find a wise man to be in charge of all this food storage." Pharaoh thought as he searched the eyes of young, wise Joseph and spoke, "Can we find *such a one* as this *is,* a man in whom the spirit of God *is*?" He then appointed Joseph to be this man.

Thus Joseph had moved from the pit into which his brothers had thrown him, all the way to becoming the first assistant to Pharaoh of Egypt. It is amazing to see what God can do when allowed to become part of a person's life. Satan may think he is winning at times, but in the long run, God will help those who are faithful and never give up hope.

THINK ABOUT IT

1. Why do you feel Joseph's brothers were so cruel to him? How can you and I make sure that we don't get jealous of other people?
2. Was there anyone who could help a lonely slave boy in a strange country? Are we ever really alone?
3. How could a young man like Joseph interpret dreams when all the wise men in Egypt could not?
4. Why do you feel Joseph was able to become a great man in Egypt? How can you and I be more like Joseph?

FORGIVENESS AND HAPPINESS
Genesis Chapters 41-45

God had spoken to Pharaoh through Joseph. There were indeed seven good years, and then came the dry, discouraging famine. Because Pharaoh had listened to Joseph and stored away great amounts of food and grain, all those in Egypt were never hungry.

Northward in the Promised Land, however, Jacob and his eleven sons would shortly be running out of food. Thus Jacob decided that ten sons should go to Egypt to buy food. Only Benjamin, Joseph's younger brother, would stay at home. He too wanted to go, but Jacob had never recovered from his sadness over losing Joseph and couldn't bear the thought of losing Benjamin as well.

The brothers arrived in Egypt and knelt before Joseph, not knowing who he was. Joseph could have hated his brothers, but his love for God was so strong that he didn't hate anyone, especially his brothers.

Without telling his brothers who he was, Joseph told them he'd give them food this time, but if they were to come again they would have to bring their youngest brother, Benjamin, with them to prove they were not spies. The brothers talked among themselves and said to each other something such as, "We can't bring him. Father has been so sad about Joseph, we can't hurt him again like we did before. If anything ever happened to Benjamin, father would die of a broken heart."

Joseph overheard these things and could
tell his brothers had changed. He went to a
place where no one could see, and there he
cried with happiness to see his brothers sorry
for the cruel things they had once done. He
wanted to embrace them and tell them not to
worry anymore. He wanted them to know who
he was and that he was safe and well, but
before that time would come the brothers had
a few more tests to pass.

When it was time to send to Egypt for more food, Jacob cried for he knew he must let his dear son, Benjamin, go. He felt strongly that if something happened to Benjamin, he would die himself. Still, there was no choice, for the family would soon starve.

Again the brothers, this time all eleven, went to Egypt. Joseph had his servants prepare a delicious dinner for his approaching guests. Upon their arrival Joseph saw his dearest brother, his boyhood friend, Benjamin. Again it was more than he could bear. He left the room and tears flowed down his face. Never had he been so happy as when he saw his younger brother.

After washing the tears from his face, Joseph returned and watched while his brothers ate. While they did so, Joseph told his workers to put food in the sacks of each brother but to put a valuable silver cup into Benjamin's sack.

The next morning the eleven brothers left for home. Their hearts were happy for they had been well-treated in Egypt. Now they were going home and the fear that something might happen to Benjamin was no longer present.

Then the brothers heard someone coming rapidly from behind. They stopped and waited as the Egyptian soldiers caught up with them and began to search through their sacks. "Here it is!" cried a soldier. "Here is the cup they have stolen." A silver cup had been found in Benjamin's sack and he was arrested. All of them were then led back to Joseph's house.

Soon they were again standing before Joseph. Judah, one of the brothers, spoke. "You once asked us about our father. We have a father, an old man, who had two sons from a wife he loved most dearly. One of those sons is dead and he now has only one son left of his favorite wife. Judah said many more things that touched Joseph's heart and finally said, "Now therefore, I pray thee, let thy servant [me] abide instead of the lad . . . and let the lad go up with his brethren."

Joseph could no longer hold back his emotions: ". . . and he cried, Cause every man to go out from me. And there stood no man with him, while Joseph made himself known unto his brethren." He was so overcome with happiness that as he wept, all in the palace could hear. He said amidst his tears, "I *am* Joseph. . . ."

As the family talked, Joseph told his brothers not to worry about the past. He told them that God had actually sent him to Egypt and had made it possible that he could keep them from starving.

Because the famine was still going on, Joseph told his brothers to go home and ask their father, Jacob, and all of the family to come and live in Egypt. When the brothers arrived in their own land they hurried to their father and said: "Father, Father! We have great news! Joseph, your beloved son, is not dead; he is alive! He is a ruler in Egypt!"

Jacob could not believe them at first. The news was too good to be true. Was his son Joseph actually alive? Jacob's hands trembled with old age and excitement, but his voice was firm and clear as he looked toward heaven and shouted, "Joseph my son *is* yet alive: I will go and see him before I die."

THINK ABOUT IT

1. Joseph had changed while he was in Egypt. He had started as a slave and was now a great leader. Had his brothers also changed? How?

62

2. Some feel that the story of Joseph and his brothers is one of the happiest stories in the Bible. Do you agree? Why?
3. Who do you feel was the happiest in this story? Was it Joseph? Was it the brothers? Was it the father? Why?

THERE IS ALWAYS HOPE
Genesis Chapters 46-50, Exodus Chapters 1, 2

With great anticipation Jacob and his family moved to Egypt. Now the new home of the Israelites (all of Israel's family) was in Egypt.

After several years of happiness in Egypt, Jacob died. His body was carried back by Joseph and others to the land he loved—the Promised Land—the land of Abraham, of Isaac, and of Jacob.

Many years passed and finally the slave boy who had become a ruler in Egypt died. After his death, a Pharaoh came into power who had not known Joseph. After some 400 years of life in Egypt things had changed for the Israelites. They had become slaves.

One day as Pharaoh was making a tour through his land he noticed that there seemed to be Israelites everywhere. He became alarmed as he thought, "There are so many of these lowly people. If they continue to increase and start an uprising, their sheer numbers alone could make them a powerful enemy."

With this fearful thought Pharaoh decided upon a most evil plan. Every baby boy born to a Hebrew [Israelite] woman was to be killed, thus the threat of the Israelites outnumbering and overpowering the Egyptians would be stopped.

God had not forgotten his people. Egypt was not their home and they were not to be slaves. They were to return to the land of promise, but in order to do this they needed a leader. In his wisdom God sent a baby who would grow up to be strong enough to lead God's people, the Israelites, back home. This baby would become his servant and be a mighty prophet.

And so it was. A boy was born who was later named Moses. Moses would do much if he lived, but he was a baby boy and Pharaoh wanted all Israelite baby boys killed.

Moses had a very clever mother and a brave older sister. A basket was woven and sealed with slime and pitch (black tar) to be a small boat. They placed Moses in the little ark and then launched its small captain in a special place very near to where the Pharaoh's daughter came each day to bathe.

Miriam, Moses' sister, hiding in some bushes nearby, heard the laughter of the princess and her friends. Then she heard someone shout out excitedly, "Look, it's a small boat. Let's get it." When the women looked inside they found the baby.

71

Soon Moses was in the arms of the princess. "What will we do with him? I know. I'll raise him as my own. But how can I care for him while he is young? He needs a woman to nurse him."

Miriam ran over and said, "I will find a woman to nurse him." Moses' mother was sent for and, although Moses' real mother took him home and kept him there a short time, from that time on Moses was the adopted son of the daughter of Pharaoh!

THINK ABOUT IT

1. How does the story of the birth of Moses show us that God is patient in his planning for what needs to be done?
2. Who do you think helped the mother and sister of Moses by giving them ideas on how to save the baby from being killed?
3. Do you feel that there are children alive today who will someday become great leaders and help God's people as Moses did?

GETTING TO KNOW GOD
Exodus Chapters 2, 3

The first forty years of the life of Moses was a time of preparation. After living briefly in his own home, Moses then moved into the royal palace, where he was trained as a prince of Egypt. During this training period he did not forget his own people—the Israelites. He was troubled by the harsh treatment they received at the hands of the Egyptians.

One day Moses became angry when he saw an Egyptian beating an Israelite. In order to save the Israelite, he struck the Egyptian with a mighty blow. He then discovered the Egyptian was dead and hoped no one had seen what had happened. Someone had seen though, and soon everyone knew. This event changed the direction of Moses' life, for he had to flee to the desert wilderness for safety.

During the next forty years Moses stayed in the wilderness as a shepherd. He worked for a man named Jethro and married his daughter Zipporah. All this time he remembered his people and the cruel treatment they were receiving from the Egyptians. He wanted them to be free.

When Moses was eighty years old another important event happened which changed his life once again. While herding his sheep, he saw a bush on fire, but it was not being consumed. "And the angel of the Lord appeared unto him in a flame of fire out of the midst of a bush. . . . God called unto him out of the midst of the bush, and said, Moses, Moses. And he said, Here *am* I."

All was ready. The baby that had been born and placed adrift in the river had grown into a man and a prophet!

THE POWER OF GOD
Exodus Chapters 4-10

Moses, like anyone else, was a mixture of faith and fear. He knew God would bless him, but he also felt a weakness in that he couldn't speak well. He asked God for help and God gave him his brother Aaron.

Aaron was very good with words. Moses would be the powerful prophet and Aaron would be the spokesman.

With Aaron at his side Moses crossed the desert and entered Egypt. The Israelites would soon be set free.

Yet freedom did not come easily. Pharaoh did not want to lose his slaves. There were cities to be built and the slaves were the power that would make the huge stones for pyramids and palaces and place them on top of each other. Pharaoh did not want to let these hardworking slaves go.

A great battle began; not a battle
of soldiers, but a battle of God working
through Moses against Satan working
through the mighty and evil Pharaoh.

81

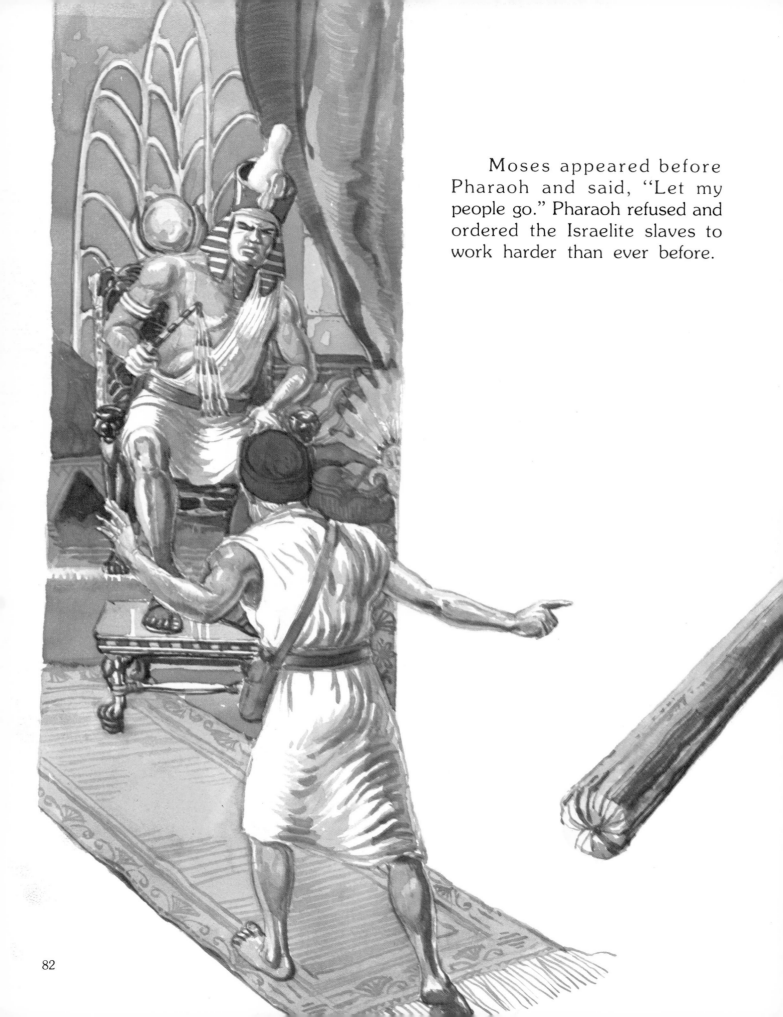

Moses appeared before Pharaoh and said, "Let my people go." Pharaoh refused and ordered the Israelite slaves to work harder than ever before.

To convince Pharaoh to let the Israelites go, Moses used the powers given him by God to cause a series of terrible things to happen in Egypt.

First the Nile river turned to blood. Then came millions of frogs—everywhere!

After that came the lice (tiny bugs which bite and itch). Frogs are ugly, but lice are a torment beyond description.

Flies came next. Swarms and swarms of miserable, dirty flies. With each affliction Moses said, "Let my people go!" Each time hardhearted Pharaoh replied, "No!"

Then God caused the cattle belonging to the Egyptians to die.

This was followed by other afflictions, such as boils (painful pus-filled sores) that appeared on the bodies of all the Egyptians.

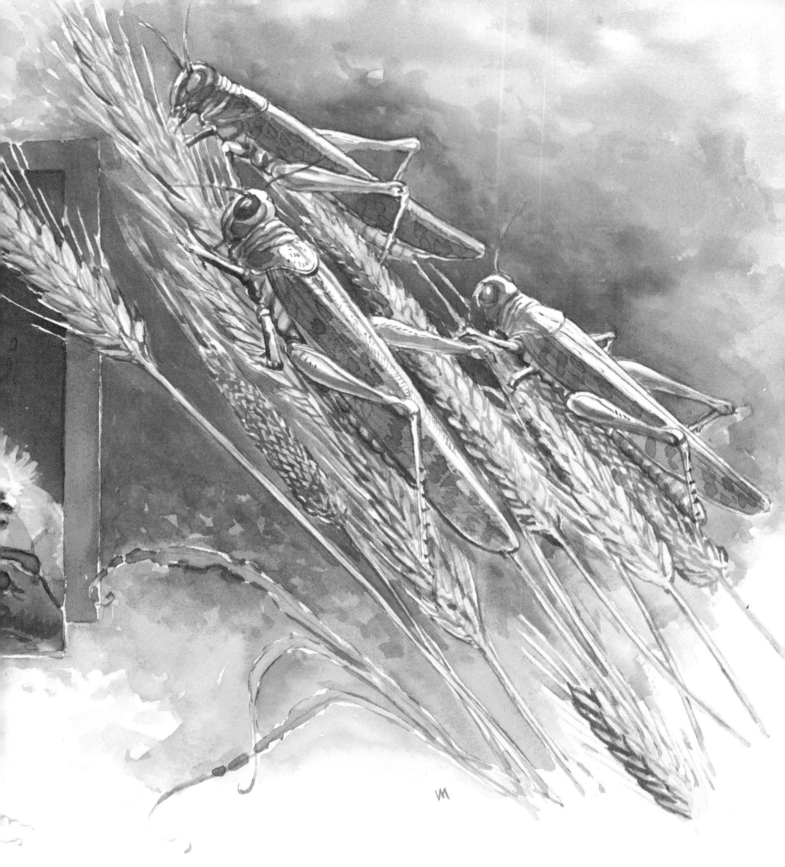

Hail fell next, which broke down trees. Locusts then swarmed, eating every living plant.

After all this there were three days of awful, depressing darkness— so dark that people could not see each other.

This was too much. Pharaoh shouted in anger, "Go serve the Lord." Yet he refused to let the Israelites take their cattle.

Moses was disappointed. His people needed the cattle or they would have no food. Then came the most terrible plague of all. It was a plague through which God showed that his power to save his people was far greater than the power of Satan to destroy them.

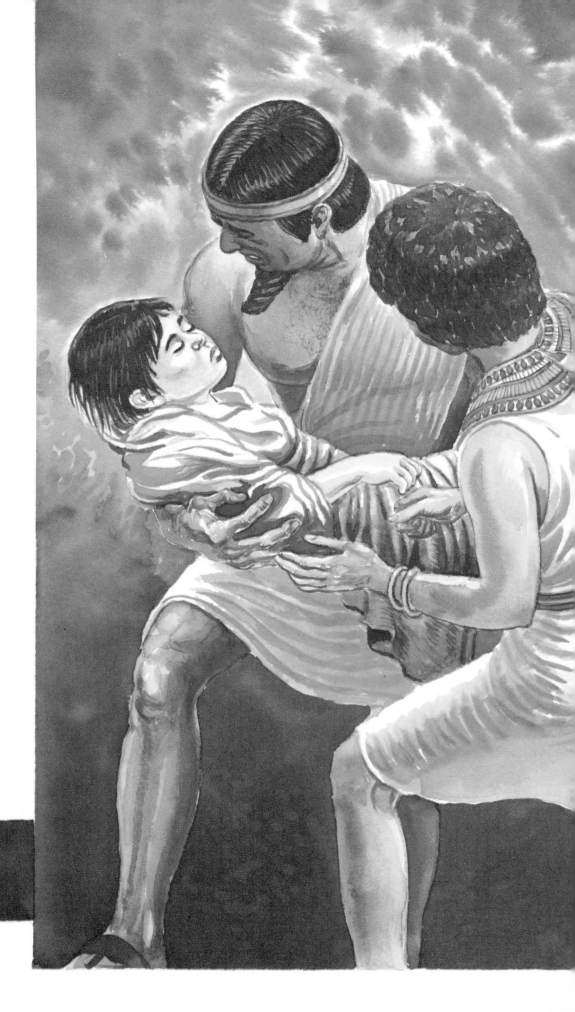

THE GIFT OF FREEDOM
Exodus Chapters 11-15

It seemed that Pharaoh and Satan were partners. This is why Pharaoh was so stubborn. Satan kept telling him, "Don't let them go." But what happened on a dark night in Egypt was more than Pharaoh could stand. On this night the worst plague in all of history struck at each Egyptian home. The oldest child in each family suddenly died. Pharaoh, after seeing his own son die, sent word to Moses:

"Rise up, *and* get you forth from among my people. . . . take your flocks and your herds, as ye have said, and be gone. . . ."

The Israelites packed and prepared to leave and gathered in large numbers to begin their journey to freedom. They talked about how Moses had told them to save themselves and their families by obediently killing a lamb and sprinkling its blood on their doorway. The blood was a sign to the destroying angel of the Lord to spare the life of the oldest child of each Israelite family in that house.

As they began their journey they could hear the sad cries of the Egyptian families who had discovered their dead children. In the years to come the Israelites would remember this night by eating a special feast to remind them of the night the Lord "smote all the firstborn in the land of Egypt" and passed over the Israelite doorways that were marked with the blood of a lamb.

After four hundred and thirty years in Egypt the Israelites were now headed home to the Promised Land. Their journey would be harder than any of them knew. It would also be forty long years before it ended.

It is hard to believe, even after all that had happened,
Satan once again convinced Pharaoh to change his mind.
The Egyptian shouted at his generals, "Go get them and
bring them back!"

Panic swept through the Israelite camp as word
spread that the Egyptian army was coming. Only Moses,
who had seen the Lord at work many times before, was
not afraid as he said, "Fear ye not. . . . The Lord shall fight
for you. . . ."

By now the Israelites were at the shores of a large body of water called the Red Sea. They could go no further. The Egyptians were getting closer and closer. It looked as though the end had come for this people who had had such high hopes.

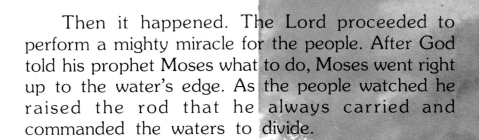

Then it happened. The Lord proceeded to perform a mighty miracle for the people. After God told his prophet Moses what to do, Moses went right up to the water's edge. As the people watched he raised the rod that he always carried and commanded the waters to divide.

To the amazement of all the Israelites the waters of the Red Sea separated! A highway of dry ground with huge walls of water on each side appeared. The Israelites cheered as they hurried into the new passageway.

The Egyptian army, seeing the dry highway in the sea, paused and then followed where the Israelites had gone. When Pharaoh's entire army had entered between the walls of water, the force that was holding the waves back suddenly was there no longer. The sea came back together and all of the Egyptian army drowned, having no chance to escape.

Sometimes people today are like the Israelites. They too are at times surrounded by problems and don't know what to do. But if they are faithful, as Moses was, the Lord will open a way for them as he did for his people many years ago.

THINK ABOUT IT

1. While Moses was a shepherd, something happened that gave him great faith in God. What was it?
2. Moses was willing to help his people but didn't feel that he was a good speaker. How did God help him?

3. If you have a brother, do you feel that the two of you could work together as Moses and Aaron did?
4. God inspired Moses and Aaron, but who was it that made Pharaoh so cruel? Why do you think Moses and Aaron finally won the battle with Pharaoh?
5. Why did the Lord open the waters of the Red Sea and let the Israelites pass through? Does he help us today in smaller but real ways?

FOOD FROM HEAVEN
Exodus Chapter 16

The Israelite fathers, mothers, and children must have felt happy as they walked toward the Promised Land. A small child might have asked, "Mother, how long will it be before we get to where we are going?" She might have answered, "Only a few weeks my child. It is not far."

The hot desert sun burned and blistered the tired travelers as they walked slowly across the hot sand. There were no trees or grass and very little water. Children cried and parents became discouraged. Some even began to wish they were back in Egypt.

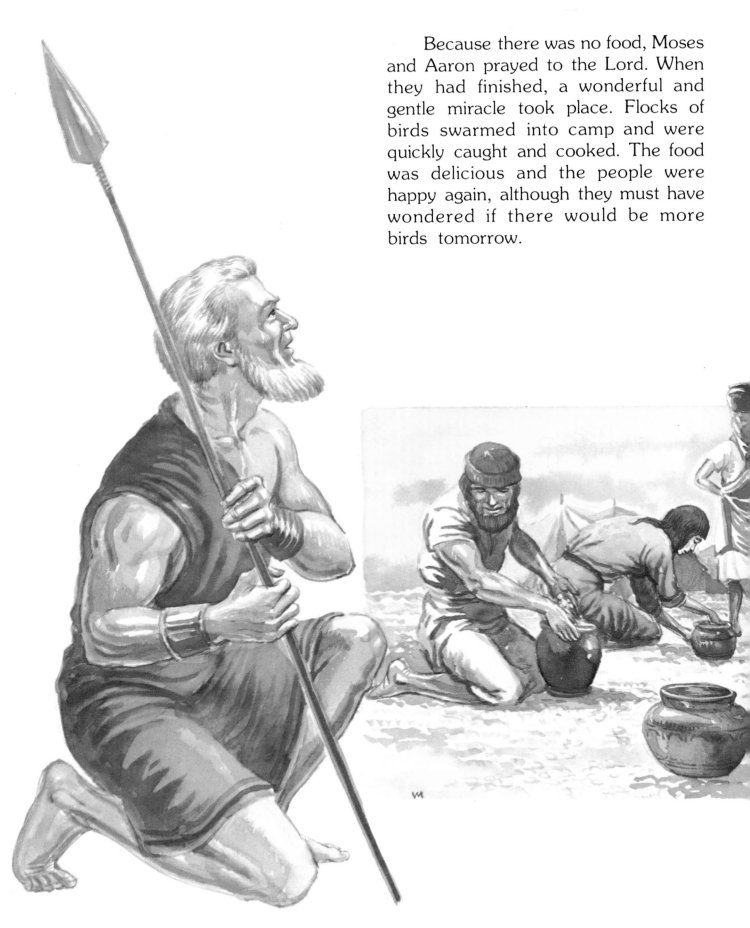

Because there was no food, Moses and Aaron prayed to the Lord. When they had finished, a wonderful and gentle miracle took place. Flocks of birds swarmed into camp and were quickly caught and cooked. The food was delicious and the people were happy again, although they must have wondered if there would be more birds tomorrow.

The next morning the people were awakened by shouts of "What is it? It is white and delicious." As they all scooped the white substance up and ate it, someone said, "It is manna." Moses added, "This *is* the bread which the Lord hath given you to eat."

AN INSPIRED BATTLE
Exodus Chapter 17

Sometime later, as God's chosen people were camped near some springs of water, all seemed well. Then news spread that an army of Arabs was about to attack them. Joshua, the general of Moses' army, quickly called the soldiers together to attack the invading enemy.

Moses was on a hill watching. As he gazed at the battle he discovered a strange thing. When he held his arms outstretched, his army would begin to win; when he lowered his arms, the enemy would push his army back. He tried his best to hold his arms up, but they became so tired he could not do it any longer.

He sat down on a rock and told Aaron to hold up one of his arms and another man to do the same with the other arm. The enemy army was then defeated and its men ran for their lives.

THINK ABOUT IT

1. Do you think manna would taste good? Why?
2. Had you been there, would you have been willing to help a prophet? Why?

THE HEAVENS OPEN
Exodus Chapters 19, 20

Around ninety days after leaving Egypt, Moses and his people looked up at the steep, rugged sides of the sacred mountain called Sinai. All mountains seem to be good places to worship God because their great height is a symbol of God's mighty power. Moses, therefore, desiring to pray to God, climbed to the top of this holy mountain.

It was there that God again spoke to his prophet, saying, ". . . if ye will obey my voice indeed, and keep my covenant, then ye shall be a peculiar treasure unto me above all people . . . and an holy nation." This is the same promise that God had given to Abraham, Isaac, and Jacob. Now Moses was being told to keep the covenant with the Lord. A covenant is a promise between a person and God. If the person promises to keep God's commandments, then God promises he will bless that person.

When Moses came down from the mountain he told the people what had happened. He said, "Will you keep the covenant or promise?" They replied, "All that the Lord hath spoken we will do."

The people were excited as Moses told them that in three days God would again speak to him in their presence. He told them to get ready for this sacred event.

Moses told the people to wash their clothes and cleanse themselves in preparation for the event, which they did during the next two days. They wanted to be clean and pure when the Lord came to visit them.

"And it came to pass on the third day in the morning, that there were thunders and lightnings, and a thick cloud upon the mount and the voice of the trumpet exceeding loud; so that all the people that *was* in the camp trembled. And Moses brought forth the people out of the camp to meet with God . . . " (Exodus 19:16, 17)

The Israelites knew that God is real and cares about his people. As they watched, Moses climbed to the top of the sacred mountain.

There in that sacred place God gave a special message to the prophet Moses. This message was one of the greatest revelations ever given to man! It was the Ten Commandments.

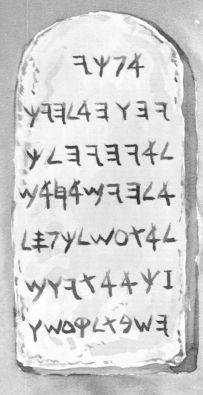

Suddenly, amid the thunder and the lightning, the Lord's finger wrote these words on a flat piece of stone:

"Thou shalt have no other gods before me.
Thou shalt not make unto thee any graven image. . . .
Thou shalt not take the name of the Lord thy God in vain. . . .
Remember the sabbath day, to keep it holy. . . .
Honour thy father and thy mother. . . .
Thou shalt not kill.
Thou shalt not commit adultery.
Thou shalt not steal.
Thou shalt not bear false witness. . . .
Thou shalt not covet. . . ."

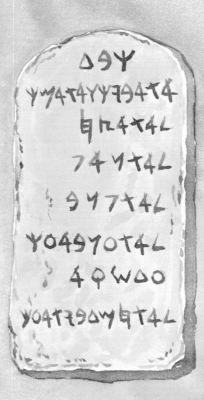

Moses and his people now knew what they needed to do to be happy. If they would worship God, be good to their parents, and have respect for each other, God would bless them. The Ten Commandments were the most fundamental set of laws ever given. If a person keeps God's commandments, he will have peace and happiness in this life and in the life to come.

Moses spoke to God many times. He wrote God's instructions to his people in five of the great books of the Bible: Genesis, Exodus, Leviticus, Numbers, and Deuteronomy. These five books are sometimes called the Law because so many of the laws that the Israelites tried to obey until the time of Jesus Christ are written in them.

When Jesus Christ was born, the Law changed somewhat, but more will be said of that later when the exciting events at Jesus' birth are presented.

THINK ABOUT IT

1. Have you ever made a covenant with the Lord? If you did or if you have, are you doing what you had told the Lord you would? Why?
2. Which of the Ten Commandments do you feel is the most important one? Why?

GETTING ORGANIZED
Exodus Chapter 18

All the people traveling with Moses wanted to shake his hand and talk to him. They felt that if they could just talk to him privately, he would solve all of their problems.

Because Moses loved his people, he spent hours talking to each one. People waited in long lines to see their wise and kind leader. Jethro, Moses' father-in-law, worried about this. He knew this was too hard on Moses and felt that if Moses became too tired he would die.

Jethro spoke to Moses and said, "Thou wilt surely wear away. . . ." He added, "Choose good men to help you. Put one man over 1000 people; then put ten men under him and have each one work with 100 people; then put ten more under each of these ten and have each one work with only ten people."

Moses liked the idea. The Israelites were organized in such a way that if a person had a problem he took it to a leader over ten. If this leader couldn't help the man, the problem was

taken to a leader over 100; if this leader couldn't help, it was taken to a leader over 1000. Finally, if needed, the matter was taken to Moses. Thus only the most difficult problems were presented to Moses.

All men need someone like Jethro to help them organize things in an orderly way.

WORSHIPPING GOD
Exodus Chapters 25-31, Numbers Chapter 12

Moses and his people wanted a building in which they could honor God, but they were always camping and then moving. How could they build it?

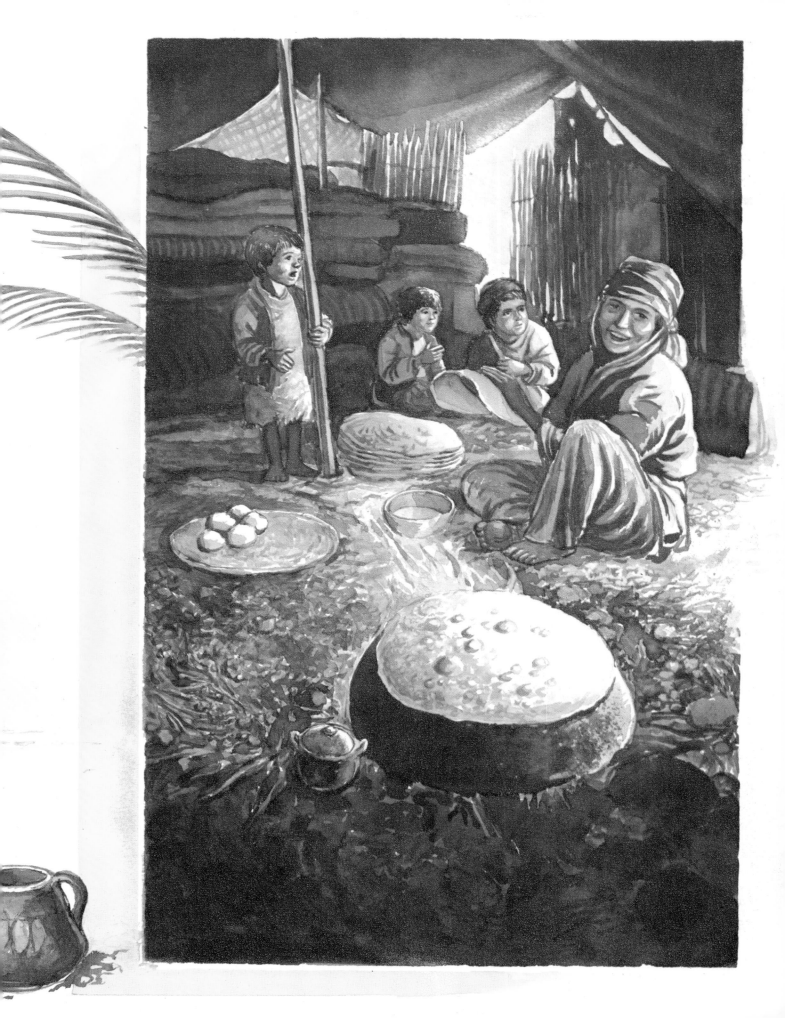

God spoke to Moses and told him to build a chapel out of canvas. The tent-like church was to be called a tabernacle. The tabernacle was divided into three parts: the court, the holy place, and the Holy of Holies.

This building was most sacred. Just as Adam, Abraham, Isaac, and Jacob had offered animals as sacrifices to God, this was also done

in the tabernacle by the Israelites as they wandered in the wilderness. This, along with other things done in the tabernacle, reminded them of God and of the Savior, who would someday be born and sacrificed for all mankind.

With a good organization, with manna from heaven, with a beautiful tabernacle, and with a great prophet, the Israelites should have been happy. That was not always the case. The people sometimes complained, which deeply saddened Moses. Even his brother Aaron and his sister Miriam complained against him.

His brother and sister told the people they did not think Moses was leading them in the right way. They said, "Hath the Lord indeed spoken only by Moses?" The Lord was not pleased with the way Aaron and Miriam were behaving. He spoke to them and told them, "My servant Moses . . . is faithful. . . . With him will I speak. . . ." He told these unfaithful people they should not speak against Moses.

Miriam then became very ill. Her skin became white and dead with a strange disease called leprosy. When Aaron saw her he was shocked and deeply sorry, for he knew the disease came because the two of them had spoken against Moses. In his sadness he cried out to Moses, "Let her not be as one dead. . . ." Moses' heart was touched. He prayed to the Lord and seven days later Miriam was healed.

Sometimes prophets told a person to do a difficult thing. Sometimes that person rebelled and said, "Who is he to tell me what to do?" No one should ever make the mistake Aaron and Miriam made. When God spoke through his prophets everyone should have listened to what he said, and obeyed him.

THINK ABOUT IT

1. Could Moses do all the Lord's work or did he need help? Which of us should help the Lord do his work?

PREVIEW OF THINGS TO COME

In Volume Three the Israelites nearly end their journey as they are near the boarders of the Promised Land. Before they enter their new home Moses sends twelve spies to see what the land is like and what kind of people live there. They return and report that the people there are giants. Because the Israelites are afraid, they do not have the faith to go on and must return to the desert for another thirty-nine years. Before these long years are over, both Moses and Aaron die and never enter the Promised Land.

Joshua is chosen to lead the children of Israel after Moses dies. The Lord performs some great miracles through him just as he did through Moses. When God's people finally enter Canaan, they have to cross over the Jordan River. Then a great miracle occurs. The river stops as if by an invisible dam and they all cross on dry ground. The walls of Jericho fall and the children of Israel conquer this fortified city without any fighting. Even though Joshua was a great prophet, he is fooled by some crafty men and moldy bread. This happens because he depends on his own judgement rather than listening to God. Later God causes the sun to stand still at Joshua's command. Finally, after many problems, Joshua and the children of Israel win their way into the beautiful Promised Land of Canaan. In their new home they divide the land between the twelve tribes of Israel. Years pass and Joshua dies, after which the Israelites gradually forget God and slip into the ways of the Canaanites, who worship idols.

Then a woman, whom the Lord raises up, fights a battle for the Israelites. Her name is Deborah, one of the Bible's greatest heroines.

Next, a humble man named Gideon wants to be sure the Lord will be with him if he fights against the wicked Canaanites. He tests the Lord and you will need to read the story to see the results.

Yes, Volume Three is filled with great adventure, faith, and excitement.